All To You...Live

#	Song Titles	Full Version	Chord Charts	Overhead Masters
1	Majestic	2	112	138
2	Everyday	10	114	139
3	Love The Lord	19	116	140
4	All To You	29	118	142
5	You Are The One	38	120	143
6	Amazed	51	122	144
7	For These Reasons	58	124	145
8	Surrender	65	136	146
9	Great Is Thy Faithfulness	73	126	147
10	Another Hallelujah	79	128	148
11	Son Of God	85	130	149
12	Let The Praises Ring	94	132	150
13	You Are Good	101	134	151

Transcriptions and Engravings – Ed Kerr
Editor – Rhonda Scelsi
Production Coordinator – Luke Gambill
Executive Producers – Don Moen and Craig Dunnagan

Product Information

Songbook 000768 35627 2
Listening CD...000768 35622 7
CD Trax Split..000768 35629 6
Worship Leader Assistant CD-ROM 000768 35620 3

Full album and individual matching orchestrations are also available.

These products are available from your favorite supplier or directly from Integrity Music at 1-800-239-7000. The numbers in the boxed area indicate the product number to be used when placing an order directly with Integrity Music. Visit us at www.integritymusic.com.

hosanna! music®

O LORD, our Lord, how majestic is your name in all the earth! Psalm 8:9
(NIV)

Majestic

Words and Music by
LINCOLN BREWSTER

Lord, our Lord, how ma - jes-tic is Your Name in all the earth;

4

Medley options: Let The Praises Ring; Prepare The Way (EVANS/NUZUM).

....I will follow you wherever you go. Matthew 8:19 (NIV)

Everyday

Words and Music by
JOEL HOUSTON

1. What to say,___ Lord, it's You Who gave___ me life,___ and I,

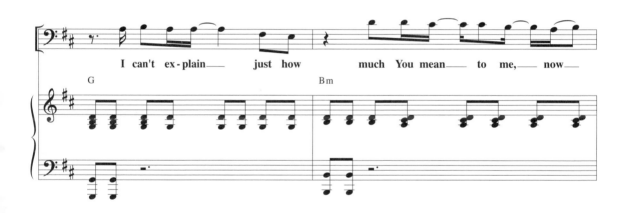

I can't ex-plain___ just how much You mean___ to me,___ now

that You have saved___ me, Lord, I give all that___ I am___ to You;

12

CHORUS

Ev - 'ry-day it's You I live for;___ Ev - 'ry-day I'll

fol - low af - ter You; Ev - 'ry-day I'll walk with You, my

Lord.___

16

18

Medley options: Celebrate The Lord Of Love; King Of Majesty.

Love the Lord your God with all your heart and with all your soul and with all
your mind and with all your strength. Mark 12:30 (NIV)

Love The Lord

**Words and Music by
LINCOLN BREWSTER**

♩ = 97

1. Love the Lord,___ your God,___ with all___ your heart, with all___ your soul,___ with all___ your mind,
2. I will serve___ the Lord with all___ my heart, with all___ my soul,___ with all___ my mind,

13 *CHORUS*

22

and with all your strength.
and with all my strength.

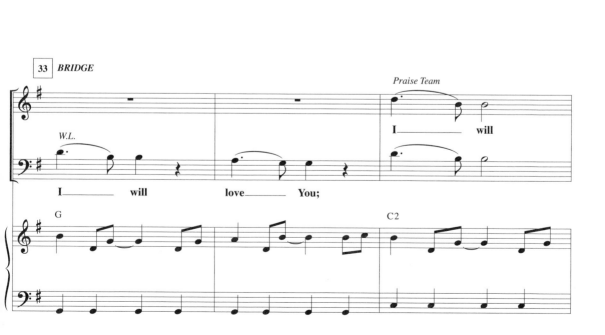

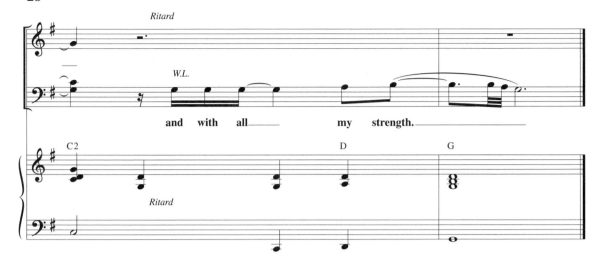

Medley options: Thank You Lord; Sing For Joy.

…Before I was born the LORD called me; from my birth he has made
mention of my name. Isaiah 49:1 (NIV)

29

All To You

Words and Music by
LINCOLN BREWSTER & REID McNULTY

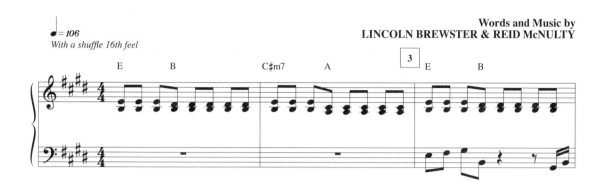

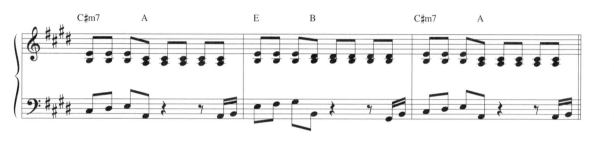

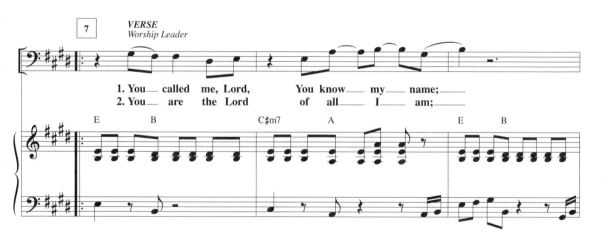

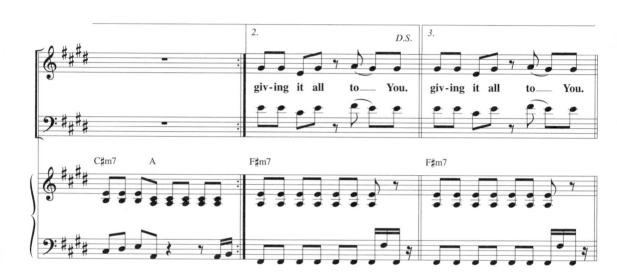

givв-ing it all to— You.   giv-ing it all to— You.

INSTRUMENTAL

Repeat as desired

I'm giv - ing it all to___ You.

75   *W.L. ad libs*

I'm liv - ing___ my___ life___ for___ You;___ I'm giv - ing___

79   *All*

ev - 'ry - thing___ to___ You;   Not hold - ing___ back,   but ev - 'ry___ part,___

Medley options: Arise; Open The Eyes Of My Heart.

You alone are the Lord. You made the heavens….the earth and all that is on it,
the seas and all that is in them…. Nehemiah 9:6 (NIV)

You Are The One

Words and Music by
PAUL BALOCHE and LINCOLN BREWSTER

40

42

You are the One   I will serve   all   my days;   You are the One,   You

F#m7   Bsus   A2

are the One,   ev-er-last   -ing;   Lord, You are the   One;

E/G#   Bsus   A2

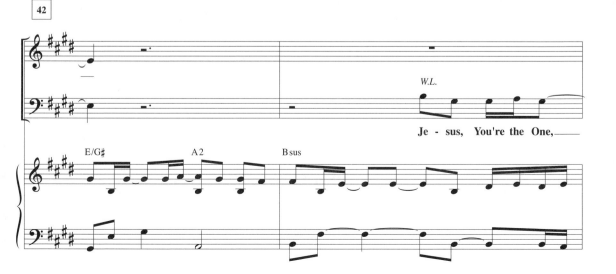

W.L.

Je - sus, You're the One,

E/G#   A2   Bsus

44

46

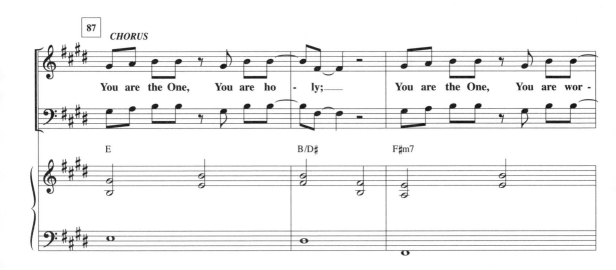

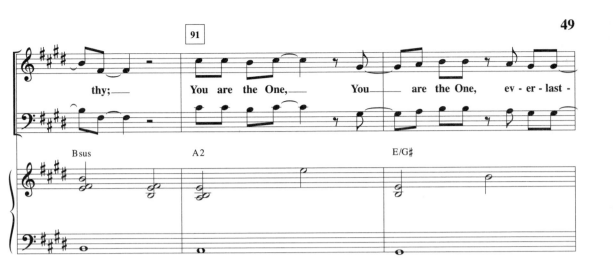

thy;—— You are the One,—— You—— are the One, ev - er - last-

B sus   A 2   E/G#

ing;—— You are the One I will wor - ship;——

B sus   A 2   E   B/D#

You are the One I will serve—— all my days;—— You are the One,—— You—

F#m7   B sus   A 2

50

Medley options: Bowing My Heart; We All Bow Down.

Amazed

Words and Music by
JARED ANDERSON

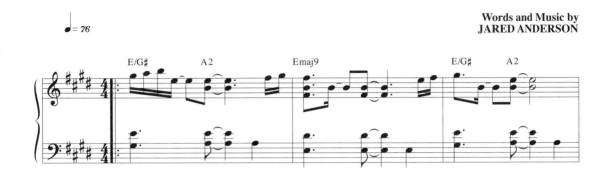

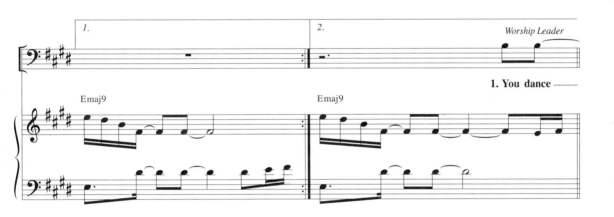

(1.)___ o - ver me___   while I___ am un - a - ware;
(2.)___ the morn - ing sky___ with mir - a - cles___ in mind;

52

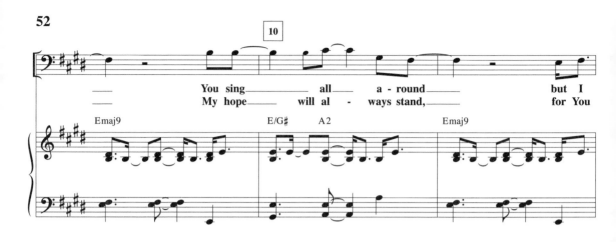

by ___ You;   Lord, I'm a-mazed _____ by ___ You,

E/G♯   A   F♯m7

___ and how   You   love _____ me; _____   How

Bsus   E

32   *BRIDGE*
Add harmonies 3rd time

deep, _____   how   wide, _____

A2   B   E/G♯

how great   is Your love for ___ me;

Lord, I'm a-mazed ___

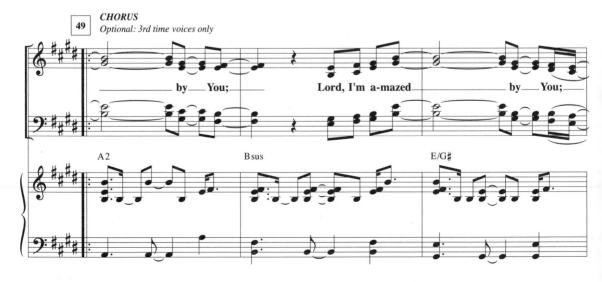

CHORUS
Optional: 3rd time voices only

_____ by ___ You; ___   Lord, I'm a-mazed ___   by ___ You;

Medley options: Worthy Is The Lamb (ZSCHECH); I Stand In Awe.

I will sing to the LORD all my life; I will sing praise to my God as long as I live.
Psalm 104:33 (NIV)

For These Reasons

Words and Music by
LINCOLN BREWSTER

60

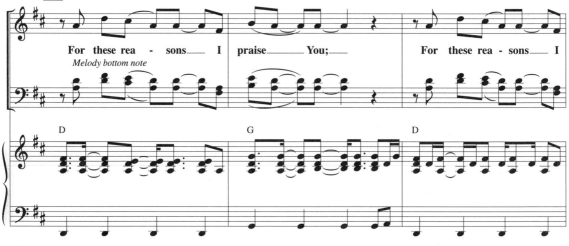

62

43 *CHORUS*

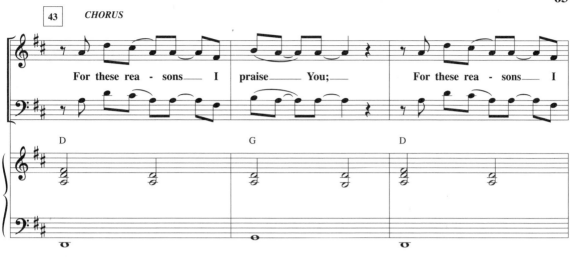

For these rea - sons___ I praise___ You;___ For these rea - sons___ I

D · G · D

47

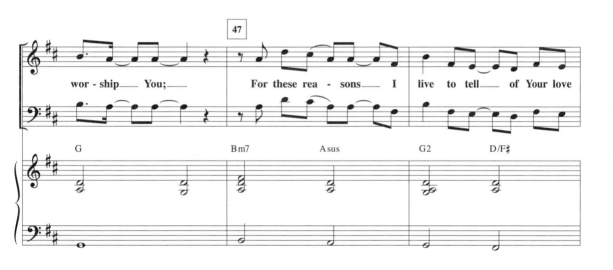

wor - ship___ You;___ For these rea - sons___ I live to tell___ of Your love

G · Bm7 · Asus · G2 · D/F♯

to all___ the world.___

Em7 · Asus · D · G2

Medley options: Prepare The Way (ANDERSON); Beautiful; Love You So Much.

Surrender

Words and Music by
MARC JAMES

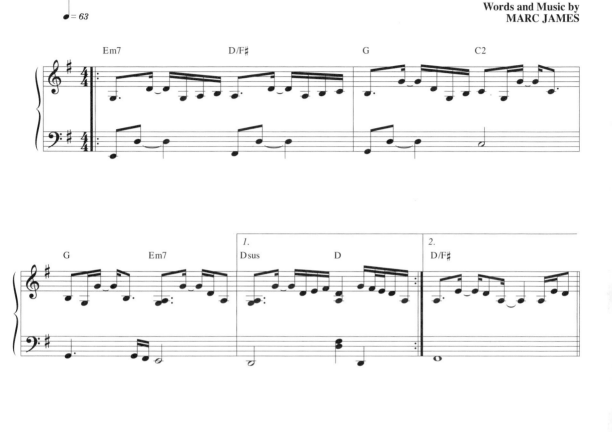

1. I'm giv-ing You___ my heart___ and all that is___ with-in;
2. I'm sing-ing You___ this song;___ I'm wait-ing at___ the cross,

I lay it all _____ down   for the sake of You, ___ my
and all the world ___ holds ___ dear,   I count it all ___ as

C2   Em7   D/F♯

King;   I'm giv-ing You___ my dreams;   I'm lay-ing down ___ my ___ rights;
loss,   for the sake of know - ing You   for the glo-ry of ___ Your ___ Name,

G   Dsus

All

And
Melody bottom note

I'm giv-ing up ___ my ___ pride,   for the prom-ise of ___ new ___ life. _____
to know the last - ing ___ joy,   e - ven shar-ing in ___ Your ___ pain. ___

C2   Em7   D/F♯   G

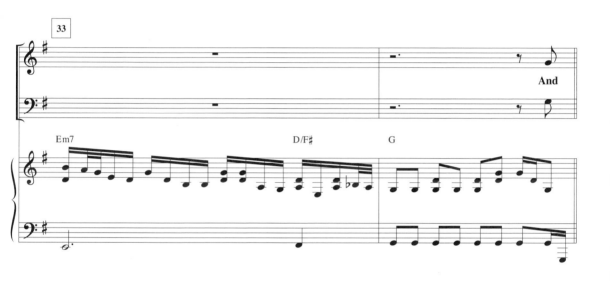

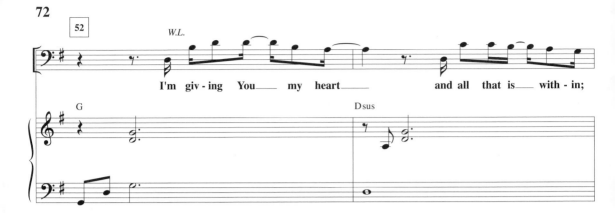

I'm giv-ing You___ my heart___ and all that is___ with-in;

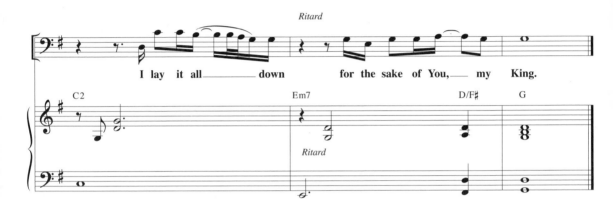

I lay it all___ down for the sake of You,___ my King.

Medley options: The Potter's Hand; Flow To You.

For great is your love, higher than the heavens; your faithfulness reaches to the skies.
Psalm 108:4 (NIV)

Great Is Thy Faithfulness

Words and Music by
THOMAS O. CHISHOLM and WILLIAM M. RUNYAN

VERSE
All

1. Great is Thy faith - ful - ness, O God, my
2. Par - don for sin, and a peace that en -

Fa - ther; There is no sha - dow of
dur - eth, Thine own dear Pres - ence to

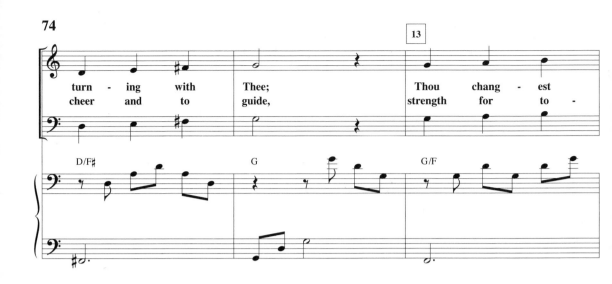

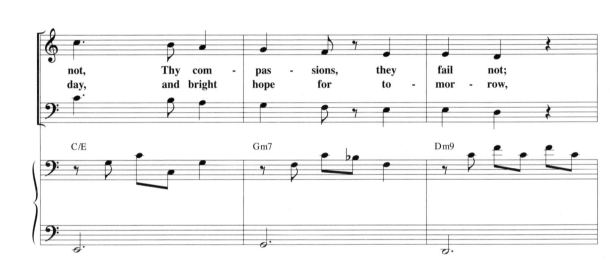

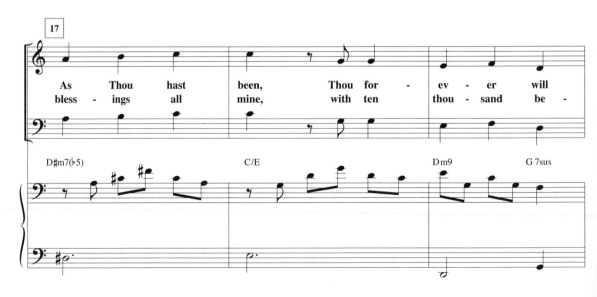

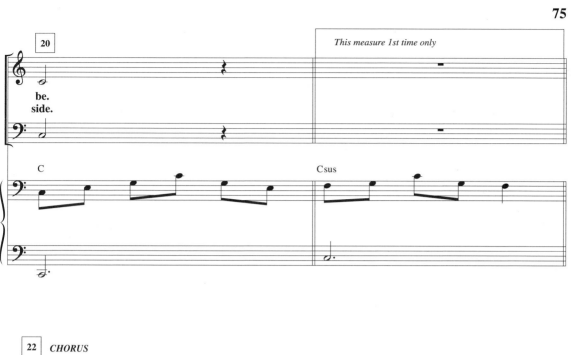

be.
side.

This measure 1st time only

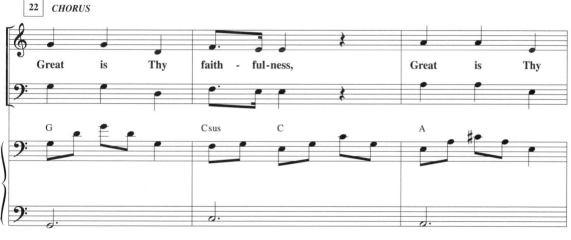

22 *CHORUS*

Great is Thy faith - ful-ness, Great is Thy

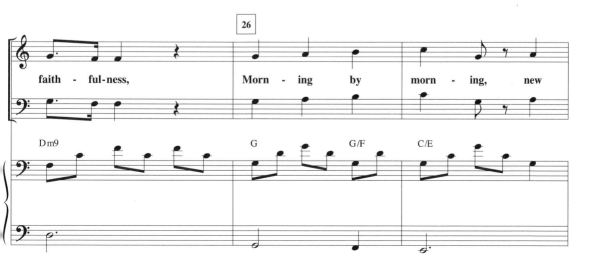

faith - ful-ness, Morn - ing by morn - ing, new

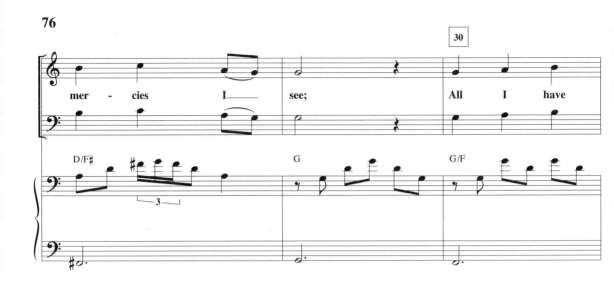

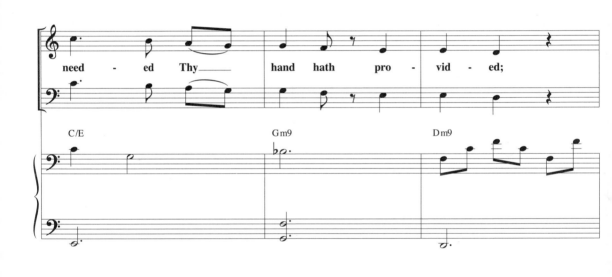

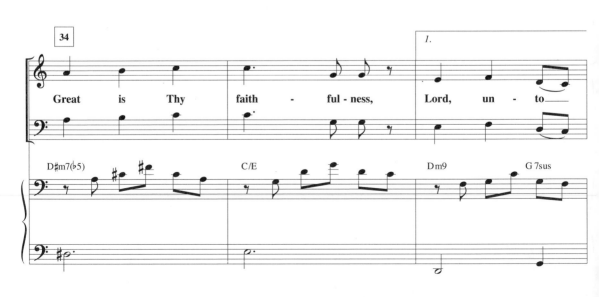

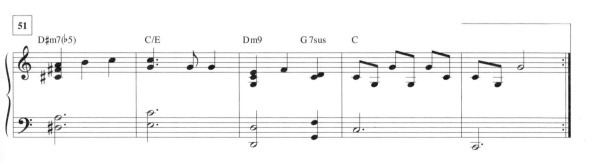

Medley options: Wonderful, Magnificent God; Blessed Be The Lord God Almighty.

He lifted me….out of the mud and mire; he set my feet on a rock and gave
me a firm place to stand. Psalm 40:2 (NIV)

Another Hallelujah

Music by
LEONARD COHEN
New lyrics by
LINCOLN BREWSTER

love You, Lord,____ with all my heart; You've giv-en me____ a
know that You're____ the God a-bove;____ You're fill-ing me____ with

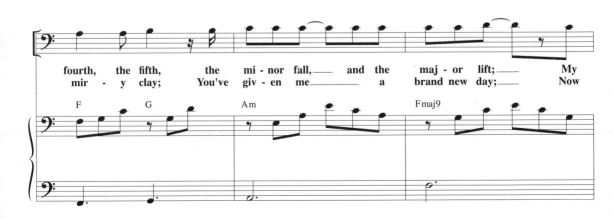

heart and soul are prais - ing, hal - le - lu - jah.
all that I can say is hal - le - lu - jah.

CHORUS

lu - jah, hal - le - lu - jah, hal - le -

lu - jah, hal - le - lu -

Last time to Coda

84

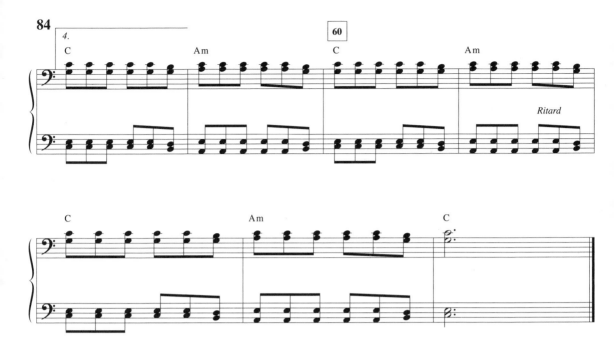

Medley options: Great Is Thy Faithfulness.

But these are written that you may believe that Jesus is the Christ, the Son of God,
and that by believing you may have life in his name. John 20:31 (NIV)

85

Son Of God

Words and Music by
LINCOLN BREWSTER and MARTY SAMPSON

1. Hold my hand and_____ walk with_____ me;
2. I need You more than_____ breath;

Je - sus, Son_____ of_____

Worship Leader cue notes

G   A

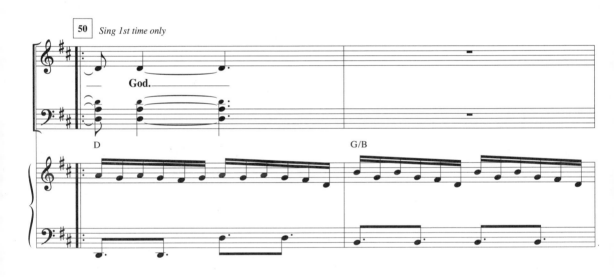

50 *Sing 1st time only*

God._____

D   G/B

A   1. D   2. D

55 *BRIDGE*

Je - sus, O, Je - sus,

D   G   Asus   A   D

59

Ho - ly is the Lamb of ——— God;

D/F♯   Bm7   Asus   A   D

63

Je - sus, O, Je - sus,

D   G   Asus   A   D

Medley options: Worthy Of Praises.

O Lord my God, in You I put my trust…. Psalm 7:1 (NKJ)

Let The Praises Ring

Words and Music by
LINCOLN BREWSTER

1. O Lord,

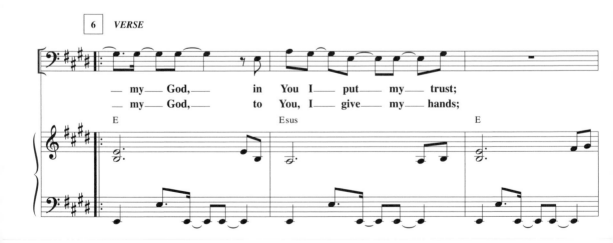

— my — God, —   in   You I — put — my — trust;
— my — God, —   to   You, I — give — my — hands;

Last time to Coda ⊕

lift up ho - ly hands and— sing   let the prais - es— ring.

A   B

38   *1.*

E   Esus   E

2.   **43**

W.L.

Let the prais - es— ring.

O, Lord, —

Esus   E   Esus

𝄌 *Coda* 55

Let the prais - es— ring;

E   Esus

Let the prais - es ring.

E   Esus   E

Medley options: Sing For Joy; Come Now Is The Time To Worship.

For the Lord is good and his love endures forever…. Psalm 100:5 (NIV)

You Are Good

**Words and Music by
ISRAEL HOUGHTON**

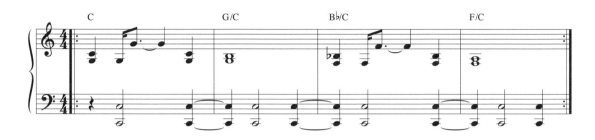

VERSE
All

Lord, You are good and Your mer-cy en-dures for-ev-er;

104

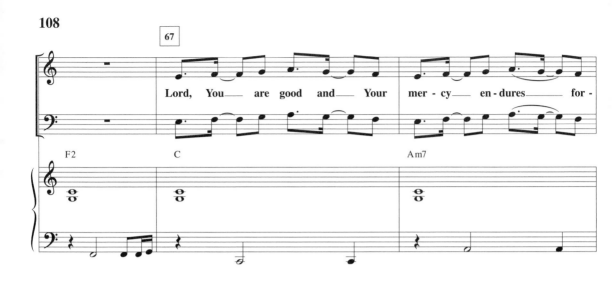

Lord, You are good and Your mer - cy en - dures for -

ev - er;___ Peo - ple___ from ev - e - ry

na - tion___ and tongue, from gen - er - a - tion to gen - er - a - tion. We

Medley options: All About You; He Will Come And Save You.

Guitar Sheets

Majestic (1 of 2)

Lincoln Brewster

INTRO
D   A   G   D   A   G   D

VERSE
D   **A**   **G**   **D**
O Lord, our Lord, how maj- estic is Your Name in all the earth
D   **A**   **G**   **D**
O Lord, our Lord, how maj- estic is Your Name in all the earth

CHORUS
               G   **D**
The heavens de- clare Your great- ness
               G   **Bm7**
The oceans cry out to You
                    G   **D/F♯**
The mountains, they bow down be- fore You
(1st ending)
     Em7   **D/F♯**   **G**   **A**   **D   A   G   D**
So I'll join with the earth and I'll give my praise to You
(Repeat Verse & Chorus)

(2nd ending)
     Em7   **D/F♯**   **G**
So I'll join with the earth and I'll sing
    A   **G**   **D**
The heavens de- clare Your great- ness
               G   **Bm7**
The oceans cry out to You
                   G   **D/F♯**
The mountains, they bow down be- fore You
     Em7   **D/F♯**   **G**   **A**   **D   A   G   D   A   G   D**
So I'll join with the earth and I'll give my praise to You

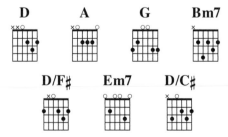

Majestic (2 of 2)

BRIDGE
```
   D           G    D           G
I will worship You, I will worship You
   D           G    D           G
I will worship You, I will worship You
   D      D/C♯   D/F♯  G
We will worship You
Bm7     D/F♯     G    A
We will worship You
```

CHORUS
```
                 G           D
The heavens de- clare Your great- ness
                   G      Bm7
The oceans cry out to You
                   G          D/F♯
The mountains, they bow down be- fore You
       Em7       D/F♯       G
So I'll join with the earth and I'll sing
      A         G           D
The heavens de- clare Your great- ness
                   G      Bm7
The oceans cry out to You
                   G          D/F♯
The mountains, they bow down be- fore You
       Em7       D/F♯       G      A     D   A
So I'll join with the earth and I'll give my praise to You
       Em7       D/F♯       G      A     D   A
So I'll join with the earth and I'll give my praise to You
       Em7       D/F♯       G      A     D
So I'll join with the earth and I'll give my praise to You
```

Everyday (1 of 2)

Joel Houston

VERSE 1

G   Bm
What to say, Lord, it's You Who gave me life and I
G   Bm
I can't explain just how much You mean to me now
G   Bm
That You have saved me, Lord, I give all that I am to You
G   Bm   G D Bm A G D Bm A
That everyday I will be a light that shines Your Name

VERSE 2

G D   Bm7 A
Ev- 'ryday, Lord, I'll learn to stand upon Your Word
G D   Bm7   A
And I pray that I, that I might come to know You more
G   D   Bm7   A
That You would guide me in every single step I take and
G D   Bm7 A   D
Ev- 'ryday I will be Your light unto the world

CHORUS

D   G   Bm7 A
Every- day it's You I live for
D   G   Bm7 A
Every- day I'll follow after You
D   G   Bm7 A   D G Bm7 A
Every- day I'll walk with You, my Lord
(Repeat Verse 2 & Chorus)

CHORUS

D   G   Bm7 A
Every- day it's You I live for
D   G   Bm7 A
Every- day I'll follow after You
D   G   Bm7 A   D G Bm7 A
Every- day I'll walk with You, my Lord

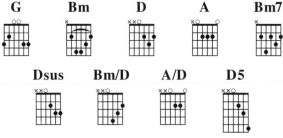

G	Bm	D	A	Bm7

Dsus	Bm/D	A/D	D5

Everyday (2 of 2)

INSTRUMENTAL
D G Bm7 A D G Bm7 A
(Repeat)

BRIDGE
     D   G   Bm7 A
It's You I live for ev- 'ry- day
     D   G   Bm7 A
It's You I live for ev- 'ry- day
     D   G   Bm7 A D G Bm7 A
It's You I live for ev- 'ry- day
(Repeat twice)

CHORUS
D   Bm7 A
Everyday it's You I live for
D   G   Bm7 A
Every- day I'll follow after You
D   G   Bm7   A   D G Bm7 A
Every- day I'll walk with You, my Lord
D   Dsus Bm/D A/D D
Every- day it's You I   live for
      Dsus Bm/D A/D   D
Every- day I'll follow   after You
      Dsus Bm/D A/D   D5
Every- day I'll walk with You, my Lord

Love The Lord (1 of 2)

Lincoln Brewster

INTRO
G   D   Em7   G/B   C2   D   G   D   C
(Repeat)

VERSE 1

  G   D   Em
Love the Lord, your God, with all your heart
            G/B   C2   D   G D C2
With all your soul, with all your mind, and with all your strength
  G   D   Em
Love the Lord, your God, with all your heart
            G/B   C2   D   G
With all your soul, with all your mind, and with all your strength

CHORUS

               C2   D
With all your heart, with all your soul
             C2/E   D/F#
With all your mind, with all your strength
  G   D   Em
Love the Lord, your God, with all your heart
            G/B   C2   D   G D C2
With all your soul, with all your mind, and with all your strength

  G D Em7 G/B C2 D G D C

VERSE 2

  G   D   Em
I will serve the Lord with all my heart
            G/B   C2   D   G D C2
With all my soul, with all my mind, and with all my strength
  G   D   Em
I will serve the Lord with all my heart
            G/B   C2   D   G
With all my soul, with all my mind, and with all my strength

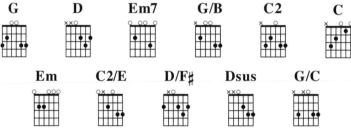

Love The Lord (2 of 2)

CHORUS
```
            C2              D
With all my heart, with all my soul
            C2/E            D/F♯
With all my mind, with all my strength
G           D               Em
I will serve the Lord with all my heart
            G/B             C2          D       G   D   C2
With all my soul, with all my mind, and with all my strength
```

INSTRUMENTAL
```
   G   G/C   Em7   G/C
```

BRIDGE
```
   G           C2
I will love You (I will love You)
Em7           C2
I will praise You (I will praise You)
G           C2
I will serve You (I will serve You)
Em7           C2     Dsus
I will trust You (I will trust You)
```

CHORUS
```
            C2              D
With all my heart, with all my soul
            C2/E            D/F♯
With all my mind, with all my strength
            C2              D
With all my heart, with all my soul
            C2/E            D/F♯
With all my mind, with all my strength
G           D               Em
I will love You,  Lord, with all my heart
            G/B             C2          D       G   D   C2
With all my soul, with all my mind, and with all my strength
G           D               Em
I will love You,  Lord, with all my heart
            G/B             C2          D       G   D   C2
With all my soul, with all my mind, and with all my strength
G           D               Em
I will love You,  Lord, with all my heart
            G/B             C2          D       G
With all my soul, with all my mind, and with all my strength
```

All To You (1 of 2)

Lincoln Brewster & Reid McNulty

INTRO
E   B   C#m7   A
(Repeat twice)

VERSE 1
E   B   C#m7 A   E   B   C#m7   A
You called me, Lord, You know my name
E B   C#m7   A   E   B   C#m7   A
I'm standing now, I'm not ashamed
                              B   E   E9
I've searched and came up empty, this world has nothing for me
A   Am
You are my One and Only

CHORUS
E B   C#m7 A
I'm   living my life for You
E B   C#m7 A
I'm   giving every- thing to You
E   B/D#   C#m7   B   A
Not hold- ing back, but eve- ry part
    F#m7   E   B   C#m7   A
I'm giving it all to You
E   B   C#m7   A   E   B   C#m7   A

VERSE 2
E   B   C#m7 A   E   B   C#m7   A
You are the Lord of   all I am
E B   C#m7   A   E   B   C#m7   A
I'll   never be the   same again
                      B
I've searched and came up empty
E   E9
This world has nothing for me
A   Am
You are my One and Only

E   B   C#m7   A   E9

Am   B/D#   F#m7   F#7   F#7/A#

All To You (2 of 2)

CHORUS
    E B   C#m7 A
    I'm   living my life for You
    E B   C#m7 A
    I'm   giving every- thing to You
    E   B/D#   C#m7   B   A
    Not hold- ing back, but eve- ry part
    (1st ending)
        F#m7   E
    I'm giving it all to You
    (Repeat Chorus)

    (2nd ending)
        F#m7
    I'm giving it all to You

INSTRUMENTAL
    C#m7   F#7   C#m7   F#7
    (Repeat as desired)

    C#m7   F#7/A#   A   F#7
    (Repeat as desired)

    E   B   C#m7   A

CHORUS
    E B   C#m7 A
    I'm   living my life for You
    E B   C#m7 A
    I'm   giving every- thing to You
    E   B/D#   C#m7   B   A
    Not hold- ing back, but eve- ry part
        F#m7
    I'm giving it all to You
    (Repeat Chorus)

    E B   C#m7 A
    I'm   living my life for You
    E B   C#m7 A
    I'm   giving every- thing to You
    E   B   C#m7   A   E   B
    Not hold- ing back, but eve- ry part
        C#m7   A
    I'm giving it all to You

    E B C#m7 A E B C#m7 A

    E B C#m7 A E B C#m7 A E

You Are The One (1 of 2)

Paul Baloche & Lincoln Brewster

INTRO
    E/G♯   A2 Bsus E/G♯ A2 Bsus

VERSE
              E/G♯   A2   Bsus
You're the One Who made the heav- ens
              E/G♯   A2   Bsus
You're the One Who shaped the earth
              E/G♯   A2   Bsus   A2   F♯m7
You're the One Who formed my heart long before my birth
         E/G♯   A2   Bsus
I be- lieve You'll al- ways lead me
            E/G♯   A2   Bsus B
All my days have been ordained
              E/G♯   A2   Bsus B   A2   F♯m7
All Your thoughts toward me are ho- ly,   full of love and grace

CHORUS
    E   B/D♯   F♯m7   Bsus
You are the One, You are ho- ly,   You are the One, You are wor- thy
    A2   E/G♯   Bsus A2
You are the One, You are the One, everlast- ing
(1st ending)
                 E/G♯ A2 Bsus   E/G♯ A2 Bsus
Lord, You are the One,   Jesus, You're the One
(Repeat Verse & Chorus)

(2nd ending)
    E   B/D♯   F♯m7   Bsus
You are the One I will wor- ship, You are the One I will serve all my days
    A2   E/G♯   Bsus A2
You are the One, You are the One, everlast- ing
                 E/G♯ A2 Bsus   E/G♯ A2 Bsus
Lord, You are the One,   Jesus, You're the One

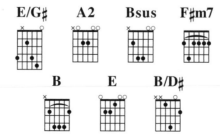

You Are The One (2 of 2)

INSTRUMENTAL
    F♯m7   E   F♯m7   A2

CHORUS
    E   **B/D♯   F♯m7**   **Bsus**
    You are the One, You are ho- ly,   You are the One, You are wor- thy
    A2   **E/G♯**   **Bsus   A2**
    You are the One, You are the One, everlast- ing
    E   **B/D♯   F♯m7**   **Bsus**
    You are the One I will wor- ship, You are the One I will serve all my days
    A2   **E/G♯**   **Bsus   A2**
    You are the One, You are the One, everlast- ing
                         E/G♯   A2   Bsus   **E/G♯   A2   Bsus**
    Lord, You are the One,   Jesus, You're the One, yeah

    E/G♯   A2   Bsus   E/G♯   A2   Bsus
    (Repeat twice)

BRIDGE
                  E/G♯   A2   Bsus   **E/G♯   A2   Bsus**
    You are the One,   You are the One
    (Repeat twice)

    E/G♯   A2   Bsus   E/G♯   A2   Bsus

CHORUS
    E   **B/D♯   F♯m7**   **Bsus**
    You are the One, You are ho- ly,   You are the One, You are wor- thy
    A2   **E/G♯**   **Bsus   A2**
    You are the One, You are the One, everlast- ing
    E   **B/D♯   F♯m7**   **Bsus**
    You are the One I will wor- ship, You are the One I will serve all my days
    A2   **E/G♯**   **Bsus   A2**
    You are the One, You are the One, everlast- ing
                         E/G♯   A2   Bsus
    Lord, You are the One
                         E/G♯   A2   Bsus
    Lord, You are the One
                         E/G♯   A2   Bsus
    Lord, You are the One
                         E
    Lord, You are the One

Amazed (1 of 2)

Jared Anderson

INTRO
E/G♯   A2   Emaj9   E/G♯   A2   Emaj9
(Repeat)

VERSE 1
       E/G♯ A2   Emaj9   E/G♯ A2   Emaj9
You dance   over me while I am   unaware
       E/G♯ A2   Emaj9   E/G♯ A2   Emaj9
You sing   all around, but I never hear the sound

CHORUS
       A2   Bsus
Lord, I'm amazed by You
       E/G♯   A
Lord I'm amazed by You
       F♯m7   Bsus
Lord, I'm amazed by You
       E
And how You love me

VERSE 2
       E/G♯ A2   Emaj9   E/G♯ A2   Emaj9
You paint the morning sky with mir- a-   cles in mind
       E/G♯   A2   Emaj9   E/G♯   A2   Emaj9
My hope will always stand, for You hold me in Your hand

CHORUS
       A2   Bsus
Lord, I'm amazed by You
       E/G♯   A
Lord I'm amazed by You
       F♯m7   Bsus
Lord, I'm amazed by You
       E
And how You love me
(Repeat Chorus)

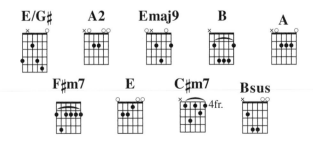

Amazed (2 of 2)

BRIDGE

A2 B   E/G♯ A2   F♯m7 B   E
How deep, how wide,   how great   is Your love for me
A2 B   E/G♯ A2   F♯m7 B   E
How deep, how wide,   how great   is Your love for me
A2 B   E/G♯ A2   F♯m7 B   E
How deep, how wide,   how great   is Your love for me
A2 B   C♯m7 Bsus F♯m7 B   E
How deep, how wide,   how   great   is Your love for me

CHORUS

                A2   Bsus
Lord, I'm amazed by You
                E/G♯ A
Lord I'm amazed by You
               F♯m7 Bsus
Lord, I'm amazed by You
                E
And how You love me
(Repeat as desired)

For These Reasons (1 of 2)

Lincoln Brewster

INTRO
    D   G   Bm7   G   D   G   Bm7   G

VERSE
        D
For Your endless love (For Your endless love)
      G2
For the life You gave (For the life You gave)
      Bm7
For the second chance (For the second chance)
      Em7   D/G
For Your priceless grace (For Your priceless grace)
      D
For Your healing hands (For Your healing hands)
      G2
For the gift of peace (For the gift of peace)
      Bm7
For the blessed hope (For the blessed hope)
      Em7   D/G
For the faith to believe (For the faith to believe)

CHORUS
    D   G
For these reasons I praise You
    D   G
For these reasons I worship You
(1st ending)
Bm7   Asus   G   D/F♯   Em7 Asus   D G Bm7   G
For these rea- sons I live to tell of Your love to all the world
(Repeat Verse & Chorus)

(2nd ending)
Bm7   Asus   G   D/F♯   Em7 Asus   D G
For these rea- sons I live to tell of Your love to all the world

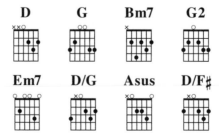

For These Reasons (2 of 2)

CHORUS
```
    D              G
For these reasons I praise You
    D              G
For these reasons I worship You
Bm7       Asus  G     D/F#      Em7  Asus    D  G  Bm7  G
For these rea- sons I live to tell of Your love to all the world
```

```
  D   G   Bm7   G
```

BRIDGE
```
    D
La da da, la da da, la da da
    G
La da da, la da da da
Bm7
La da da, la da da, la da da
```
(1st ending)
```
D/G
La da da, la da da da
```
(Repeat)

(2nd ending)
```
D/G
La da da
```

CHORUS
```
    D                 G
For these reasons I praise You
    D                 G
For these reasons I worship You
Bm7        Asus  G2    D/F#      Em7  Asus     D
For these rea- sons I live to tell of Your love to all the world
```

```
    D                    G
For these reasons we praise You
    D                    G
For these reasons we worship You
Bm7        Asus  G2    D/F#      Em7  Asus     D
For these rea- sons we live to tell of Your love to all the world
```

Surrender (1 of 2)

Marc James

INTRO
Em7   D/F♯   G   C2   G   Em7   Dsus

Em7   D/F♯   G   C2   G   Em7   D/F♯

VERSE 1
G   D   C2
I'm giving You my heart, and all that is within
         Em7   D/F♯   G
I lay it all down for the sake of You, my King
                    Dsus   C2
I'm giving You my dreams, I'm laying down my rights
              Em7   D/F♯ G
I'm giving up my pride for the promise of new   life

CHORUS
      Em7 D/F♯   G   C   G Em7 Dsus   D
And I   surren- der all to You, all to You
      Em7 D/F♯   G   C   G Em7 Dsus   D
And I   surren- der all to You, all to You

VERSE 2
G   D   C2
I'm singing You this song, I'm waiting at the cross
                       Em7   D/F♯ G
And all the world holds dear, I count it all as   loss
                    Dsus   C2
For the sake of knowing You, for the glory of Your Name
                 Em7   D/F♯   G
To know the lasting joy , even sharing in Your   pain

CHORUS
      Em7 D/F♯   G   C   G Em7 Dsus   D
And I   surren- der all to You, all to You
      Em7 D/F♯   G   C   G Em7 Dsus   D
And I   surren- der all to You, all to You
(Repeat Chorus)

Em7   D/F♯   G   C2

Dsus   D   C

© 2000 Vineyard Songs (UK/EIRE) CCLI #3033179

Surrender (2 of 2)

INSTRUMENTAL
> G   D   C   Em7   D/F♯   G   D   C   Em7   D/F♯   G

CHORUS
> **Em7 D/F♯   G   C   G Em7 Dsus**
> And I   surren- der all to You, all to You
> **Em7 D/F♯   G   C   G Em7 Dsus   D**
> And I   surren- der all to You, all to You

CHORUS
> **Em7 D/F♯   G   C   G Em7 Dsus   D**
> And I   surren- der all to You, all to You
> **Em7 D/F♯   G   C   G Em7 Dsus   D**
> And I   surren- der all to You, all to You
> *(Repeat as desired)*

> **G   Dsus   C2**
> I'm giving You my heart, and all that is within
> **Em7   D/F♯   G**
> I lay it all down for the sake of You, my King

Great Is Thy Faithfulness (1 of 2)

Thomas O. Chisholm & William M. Runyan

INTRO
  C

VERSE 1
  C   F2/A G7sus C
  Great is Thy faithfulness, O God, my Father
  F2   C/E   D/F♯   G
  There is no shadow of turning with Thee
  G/F   C/E   Gm7   Dm9
  Thou changest not, Thy com- passions, they fail not
  D♯m7(♭5) C/E   Dm9 G7sus C Csus
  As Thou hast been, Thou for- ever will   be

CHORUS
  G   Csus C A   Dm9
  Great is Thy faithful- ness, Great is Thy faithfulness
  G   G/F C/E   D/F♯ G
  Morning by morning, new mercies I see
  G/F   C/E   Gm9   Dm9
  All I have needed Thy hand hath pro- vided
  D♯m7(♭5) C/E   Dm9 G7sus C Csus
  Great is Thy faithfulness, Lord, un- to   me

INSTRUMENTAL

  C F/A Gsus Csus C F C/E D/F♯ G

  G/F C/E Gm9 Dm9 D♯m7(♭5) C/E Dm9 G7sus C

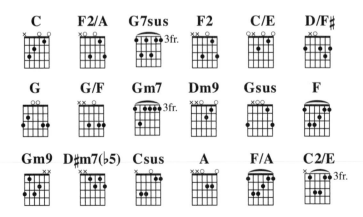

Great Is Thy Faithfulness (2 of 2)

VERSE 2

```
    C          F2/A    G7sus         C
    Pardon for sin, and a peace that en- dureth
    F2            C/E        D/F♯       G
    Thine own dear Presence to cheer and to guide
    G/F           C/E         Gm7         Dm9
    Strength for to- day, and bright hope for to- morrow
    D♯m7(♭5)    C/E          Dm9      G7sus   C
    Blessings all mine, with ten thousand be-       side
```

CHORUS

```
    G            Csus     C    A          Dm9
    Great is Thy faithful- ness, Great is Thy faithfulness
    G        G/F  C/E         D/F♯       G
    Morning by    morning, new mercies I see
    G/F       C/E         Gm9          Dm9
    All I have needed Thy hand hath pro- vided
    D♯m7(♭5)     C/E
    Great is Thy faithfulness
    D♯m7(♭5)     C/E
    Great is Thy faithfulness
    D♯m7(♭5)     C2/E         Dm9      G7sus   C
    Great is Thy faithfulness,   Lord, un- to        me
```

Another Hallelujah (1 of 2)

Music by Leonard Cohen
New lyrics by Lincoln Brewster

INTRO
    C Am C Am C Am C Am

VERSE 1
```
        C                 Am
I love You, Lord, with all my heart
        C           Am
You've given me a brand new start
       F          G            C  Am
And I just want to sing this song to You
           C            F       G      Am        Fmaj9
Well, it goes like this, the fourth, the fifth, the minor fall, the major lift
       G            E/G#         Am
My heart and soul are praising, halle- lujah
```

CHORUS
```
          Fmaj9      Am
Halle- lujah, halle- lujah
          Fmaj9      C G   C  Am  C  Am
Halle- lujah, halle- lu-    jah
```

VERSE 2
```
        C                   Am
Well, I know that You're the God above
          C            Am
You're filling me with grace and love
       F          G           C  Am
But I just want to say thank you to You
         C           F   G       Am        Fmaj9
You pulled me from the miry clay, You've given me a brand new day
       G          E/G#      Am
Now all that I can say is halle- lujah
```

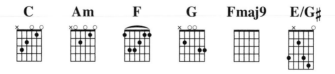

C   Am   F   G   Fmaj9   E/G♯

Another Hallelujah (2 of 2)

CHORUS

      Fmaj9   **Am**
Halle- lujah, halle- lujah
      Fmaj9   **C G** **C** **Am** **C** **Am**
Halle- lujah, halle- lu-   jah

  C **Am** **C** **Am**

CHORUS

      Fmaj9   **Am**
Halle- lujah, halle- lujah
      Fmaj9   **C G** **C** **Am** **C** **Am**
Halle- lujah, halle- lu-   jah
(Repeat as desired)

  C **Am** **C** **Am** **C**

Son Of God (1 of 2)

Lincoln Brewster & Marty Sampson

INTRO
    D

VERSE 1
    D   **D/G**   **Asus**   **D**
    Hold my hand and walk with me
    D/F♯   **D/G**   **Asus A D**
    You're the light that makes me see
             D/G   **Asus**   **D**
    On this path, my soul You lead
    D/F♯ D/G   **Asus A   D**
    O, my Shepherd, walk with me

CHORUS
       G   **D/F♯**
    My Savior, Glorious One
       G   **Asus**   **A**
    My Redeemer, living in my heart
          G   **Bm7 Asus A**
    Now and for- ever, Your Kingdom come
     G   **Asus A D G/B A D G/B A D**
    O, Jesus, Son   of God

VERSE 2
    D   **D/G Asus**   **D**
    I need You more than breath
    D/F♯   **D/G**   **Asus A D**
    You're my hope, in You   I   live
         D/G   **Asus**   **D**
    Angels worship at Your throne
    D/F♯   **D/G**   **Asus A D**
    Power and glory to You a-   lone

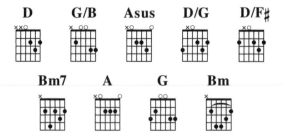

Son Of God (2 of 2)

CHORUS
```
        G              D/F#
My Savior, Glorious One
        G                   Asus    A
My Redeemer, living in my heart
                    G                   Bm7   Asus   A
Now and for- ever, Your Kingdom come
    G      Asus A  Bm   A
O, Jesus, Son      of God
    G      A     D  G/B   A   D  G/B   A   D
O, Jesus, Son of God
```

BRIDGE
```
    D  G      Asus A  D
Je- sus, O, Je-     sus
    D/F#   Bm7 Asus A  D
Holy   is the Lamb of  God
    D  G      Asus A  D
Je- sus, O, Je-     sus
    D/F#   Bm7 Asus A  D
Worthy is the Lamb of  God
(Repeat)
```

CHORUS
```
        G              D/F#
My Savior, Glorious One
        G                   Asus    A
My Redeemer, living in my heart
                    G                   Bm7   Asus   A
Now and for- ever, Your Kingdom come
    G      A     Bm   A
O, Jesus, Son of God
    G      A     D  G/B   A   D
O, Jesus, Son of God
```

OUTTRO
```
    D  G/B   A   D
(Repeat as desired)
```

Let The Praises Ring (1 of 2)

Lincoln Brewster

INTRO
    E   Esus E   Esus E   Esus E

VERSE 1
```
        E              Esus          E    Esus
O Lord, my God, in You I put my trust
        E              Esus          E    Esus
O Lord, my God, in You I put my hope
        E              Esus          E    Esus
O Lord, my God, in You I put my trust
        E              Esus          E    Esus
O Lord, my God, in You I put my hope
```

CHORUS
```
    B    C#m   A2              Esus   E
In You, in You I find my peace
    B    C#m   A2              Esus   E
In You, in You I find my strength
    B    C#m   A2              Esus   E
In You I live and move and breathe
    B    C#m                Bsus
Let everything I say and do be founded by my faith in You
    A              B             E   Esus   E   Esus
I lift up holy hands and sing let the praises ring
```

VERSE 2
```
        E              Esus          E
O Lord, my God, to You I give my hands
        E              Esus          E
O Lord, my God, to You I give my feet
        E              Esus          E    Esus
O Lord, my God, to You I give my eve- rything
        E              Esus          E
O Lord, my God, to You I give my life
```

    E   Esus   B   C#m   A2   Bsus   A

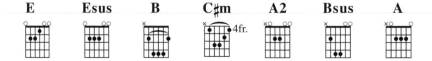

Let The Praises Ring (2 of 2)

CHORUS
    B   C♯m A2   **Esus E**
    In You, in You I find my peace
    B   C♯m A2   **Esus E**
    In You, in You I find my strength
    B   C♯m A2   **Esus E**
    In You I live and move and breathe
    B C♯m   **Bsus**
    Let everything I say and do be founded by my faith in You
     A   **B**   **E Esus**
    I lift up holy hands and sing let the praises ring
                     E Esus
    Let the praises ring

INSTRUMENTAL

    E

CHORUS
    B   C♯m A2   **Esus E**
    In You, in You I find my peace
    B   C♯m A2   **Esus E**
    In You, in You I find my strength
    B   C♯m A2   **Esus E**
    In You I live and move and breathe
    B C♯m   **Bsus**
    Let everything I say and do be founded by my faith in You
     A   **B**   **E Esus**
    I lift up holy hands and sing let the praises ring
                     E Esus
    Let the praises ring
                     E Esus
    Let the praises ring
                     E
    Let the praises ring

You Are Good (1 of 2)

Israel Houghton

INTRO
```
     C   G/C   Bb/C   F/C   C   G/C   Bb/C   F/C

     C   Gm7   Bb    F    C   Gm7   Bb    F
```

VERSE
```
     C                        Am7              Gsus   F2
     Lord, You are good and Your mercy endures for- ever
     C                        Am7              Gsus   F2
     Lord, You are good and Your mercy endures for- ever
     F              G/F              Fm7              Bb/F
     People from every nation and tongue, from generation to generation
```

CHORUS
```
        C        Gm7  Bb2        F2
     We worship You,    hallelujah, hal- lelujah
        C        Gm7            Ab
     We worship You for who You are
```
(1st ending)
```
     Bb2                  C   Gm7   Bb   F   C   Gm7   Bb   F
     'Cause You are good
```
(Repeat Verse & Chorus)

(2nd ending)
CHORUS
```
     Bb   C        Gm7  Bb2        F2
      We worship You,    hallelujah, hal- lelujah
        C        Gm7            Ab   Bb2
     We worship You for who You are        'cause You are good

     C   Eb   F   C   Eb   F
```

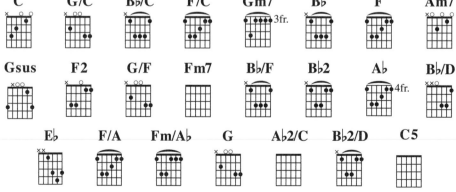

You Are Good (2 of 2)

BRIDGE
    F/A   Fm/A♭   C   E♭   F
       You are good   all the time, all the time You are good
(1st ending)
          C   E♭   F
You are good   all the time, all the time You are good
(Repeat as desired)

(2nd ending)
          C   E♭   F   **F/A**
You are good   all the time, all the time You are good

VERSE
    C   **Am7**   **Gsus   F2**
Lord, You are good and Your mercy endures for- ever
    C   **Am7**   **Gsus   F2**
Lord, You are good and Your mercy endures for- ever
    F   **G**   **Fm7**   **B♭/D**
People from every nation and tongue, from generation to generation

CHORUS
     C   **Gm7 B♭2**   **F2**
We worship You,   hallelujah, hal- lelujah
     C   **Gm7**   **A♭   B♭**
We worship You for who You are .
     C   **Gm7 B♭2**   **F2**
We worship You,   hallelujah, hal- lelujah
     C   **Gm7**   **A♭   B♭**
We worship You for who You are
         A♭2/C   **B♭2/D**
For who You are, for who You are
         Fm7   B♭2
For who You are
         C5
'Cause You are good

Overhead Masters

Majestic

(Verse)
O Lord our Lord how majestic is
Your name in all the earth
O Lord our Lord how majestic is
Your name in all the earth

(Chorus)
The heavens declare Your greatness
The oceans cry out to You
The mountains they bow down before You
So I'll join with the earth
And I'll give my praise to You

(Bridge)
I will worship You I will worship You
I will worship You I will worship You
We will worship You
We will worship You

Lincoln Brewster
© *2005 Integrity's Praise! Music/BMI*

Everyday

(Verse 1)
What to say Lord it's You Who gave me life
And I, I can't explain
Just how Much You mean to me
Now that You have saved me Lord
I give all that I am to You
That everyday I can
Be a light that shines Your name

(Verse 2 and 3)
Everyday Lord I'll learn to stand upon Your Word
And I pray that I, that I might
Come to know You more
That You would guide me in
Every single step I take and
Everyday I will be Your light unto the world

(Chorus)
Everyday it's You I live for
Everyday I'll follow after You
Everyday I'll walk with You my Lord

(Bridge)
It's You I live for everyday
It's You I live for everyday
It's You I live for everyday

Love The Lord (1 of 2)

(Verse 1)
Love the Lord Your God with all your heart
With all your soul with all your mind
And with all your strength
Love the Lord Your God with all your heart
With all your soul with all your mind
And with all your strength

(Chorus 1)
With all your heart with all your soul
With all your mind with all your strength
Love the Lord Your God with all your heart
With all your soul with all your mind
And with all your strength

(Verse 2)
I will serve You Lord with all my heart
With all my soul with all my mind
And with all my strength
I will serve You Lord with all my heart
With all my soul with all my mind
And with all my strength

Lincoln Brewster
© 2005 Integrity's Praise! Music/BMI

Love The Lord (2 of 2)

(Chorus 2)
With all my heart with all my soul
With all my mind with all my strength
I will serve You Lord with all my heart with all my soul
With all my mind and with all my strength

(Bridge)
I will love You *(echo)*
I will praise You *(echo)*
I will serve You *(echo)*
I will trust You *(echo)*

(Chorus 3)
With all my heart with all my soul
With all my mind with all my strength
(Repeat)
I will love You Lord with all my heart
With all my soul with all my mind
And with all my strength
(Repeat twice)

Lincoln Brewster
© *2005 Integrity's Praise! Music/BMI*

All To You

(Verse 1)
You called me Lord You know my name
I'm standing now I'm not ashamed
I've searched and came up empty
This world has nothing for me
You are my One and only

(Chorus)
I'm living my life for You
I'm giving everything to You
Not holding back but every part
I'm giving it all to You

(Verse 2)
You are the Lord of all I am
I'll never be the same again
I've searched and came up empty
This world has nothing for me
You are my One and only

Lincoln Brewster and Reid McNulty
© 2005 Integrity's Praise! Music/BMI

You Are The One

(Verse)
You're the One Who made the heavens
You're the One Who shaped the earth
You're the One Who formed my heart
Long before my birth
I believe You'll always lead me
All my days have been ordained
All Your thoughts toward me are holy
Full of love and grace

(Chorus 1)
You are the One You are holy
You are the One You are worthy
You are the One You are the One everlasting
Lord You are the One

(Chorus 2, 3, and 4)
You are the One You are holy
You are the One You are worthy
You are the One You are the One everlasting
You are the One I will worship
You are the One I will serve all my days
You are the One You are the one everlasting
You are the One

Paul Baloche and Lincoln Brewster
© 2002 Integrity's Hosanna! Music/ASCAP and Integrity's Praise! Music/BMI

Amazed

(Verse 1)
You dance over me while I am unaware
You sing all around but I never hear the sound

(Chorus)
Lord I'm amazed by You
Lord I'm amazed by You
Lord I'm amazed by You
And how You love me

(Verse 2)
You paint the morning sky with miracles in mind
My hope will always stand
For You Hold me in Your hand

(Bridge)
How deep how wide
How great is Your love for me

Jared Anderson
© *2003 Vertical Worship Songs/ASCAP*

For These Reasons

(Verse)
For Your endless love *(echo)*
For the life You gave *(echo)*
For the second chance *(echo)*
For Your priceless grace *(echo)*
For Your healing hands *(echo)*
For the gift of peace *(echo)*
For the blessed hope *(echo)*
For the faith to believe *(echo)*

(Chorus)
For these reasons I praise You
For these reasons I worship You
For these reasons I live to tell of Your love
To all the world

(Bridge)
La da da, la da da, la da da
La da da, la da da da

Surrender

(Verse 1)
I'm giving You my heart
And all that is within
I lay it all down
For the sake of You my King
I'm giving You my dreams
I'm laying down my rights
I'm giving up my pride
For the promise of new life

(Chorus)
I surrender all to You all to You
I surrender all to You all to You

(Verse 2)
I'm singing You this song
I'm waiting at the cross
And all the world holds dear
I count it all as loss
For the sake of knowing You
For the glory of Your name
To know the lasting joy
Even sharing in Your pain

Marc James
© *2000 Vineyard Songs (UK/Eire) Administered in North America by Music Services o/b/o Vineyard Music Global,*
Inc./PRS

Great Is Thy Faithfulness

(Verse 1)
Great is Thy faithfulness
O God my Father
There is no shadow of turning with Thee
Thou changest not
Thy compassions they fail not
As Thou hast been Thou forever will be

(Chorus)
Great is Thy faithfulness
Great is Thy faithfulness
Morning by morning new mercies I see
All I have needed Thy hand hath provided
Great is Thy faithfulness Lord unto me

(Verse 2)
Pardon for sin
And a peace that endureth
Thine own dear presence
To cheer and to guide
Strength for today
And bright hope for tomorrow
Blessings all mine
With ten thousand beside

Words: Thomas O. Chisholm
Music: William M. Runyan
© 1923, Renewed 1951 and this arrangement © 2005 by Hope Publishing Company

Another Hallelujah

(Verse 1)
I love You Lord with all my Heart
You've given me a brand new start
And I just want to sing this song to You
It goes like this the fourth the fifth
The minor fall the major lift
My heart and soul are praising
Hallelujah

(Chorus)
Hallelujah hallelujah
Hallelujah hallelujah

(Verse 2)
I know You are the God above
You're filling me with grace and love
And I just want to say thank You to You
You pulled me from the miry clay
You've given me a brand new day
Now all that I can say is
Hallelujah

Music by: Leonard Cohen
New lyrics by: Lincoln Brewster
© *1985, 2005 Bad Monk Publishing (adm by Sony/ATV Music Publishing)/BMI*

Son Of God

(Verse 1)
Hold my hand and walk with me
You're the light that makes me see
On this path my soul You lead
O my Shepherd walk with me

(Chorus)
My Savior Glorious One
My Redeemer living in my heart
Now and forever Your kingdom come
Jesus Son of God

(Verse 2)
I need You more than breath
You're my hope in You I live
Angels worship at Your throne
Power and glory to You alone

(Bridge)
Jesus O Jesus
Holy is the Lamb of God
Jesus O Jesus
Worthy is the Lamb of God

Lincoln Brewster and Marty Sampson
© *2002 Integrity's Praise! Music/BMI, Marty Sampson/Hillsong Publishing (adm in the U.S. and Canada by Integrity's Hosanna! Music)/ASCAP*

Let The Praises Ring

(Verse 1)
O Lord my God in You I put my trust
O Lord my God in You I put my hope
O Lord my God in You I put my trust
O Lord my God in You I put my hope

(Chorus)
In You in You I find my peace
In You in You I find my strength
In You I live and move and breathe
Let everything I say and do
Be founded by my faith in You
I lift up holy hands and sing
Let the praises ring

(Verse 2)
O Lord my God to You I give my hands
O Lord my God to You I give my feet
O Lord my God to You I give my everything
O Lord my God to You I give my life

Lincoln Brewster
© *2002 Integrity's Praise! Music/BMI*

You Are Good

(Verse)
Lord You are good
And Your mercy endures forever
Lord You are good
And Your mercy endures forever
People from every nation and tongue
From generation to generation

(Chorus)
We worship You
Hallelujah hallelujah
We worship You
For Who You are
'Cause You are good

(Bridge)
You are good all the time
All the time You are good

Israel Houghton
© *2001 Integrity's Praise! Music/BMI*